ALTERED MINDS

A POETRY COLLECTION

BY LOGAN SINGLETARY

The lamppost shines dimly in the dark.
Sit under the bench, wait, and watch the world move around you.
Rest and read for a while.
Open your heart, mind, and soul.
If just for a flicker of a moment, let yourself be moved.

For you, the reader.

TABLE OF CONTENTS

ALTERED MINDS

What does it mean to think?

I am aware of my thoughts,

But am I alive?

I think so.

I'm not sure how I know, but I do.

I understand what I think,

but is it even real?

Are my thoughts meaningless,

or is there a greater purpose to   breathe.

Just as the sky spins,

so does my head.

Wondering if I am here.

Heaven shines above me,

Hell shackles my mind.

Will I ever be free?

Free of my mind?

Free of my sanity?

Free of my life?

My mind is altered,

my soul must remain pure.

THE CLOCK TICKS FOR THE SOUL

A moment passes me by

                                                    Tick

If only I could pause and rest

                                                    Tock

Seconds leave me wishing for second chances

                                                    Tick

Minutes make small seem large

                                                    Tock

Hours become eternity

                                                    Tick

Sand flows away at my feet

                                                    Tock

Ensnared in glass

                                                    Tick

The shards stare within my eyes

                                                    Tock

Striking the mind, I weep

                                                    Tick

I wake with sleep

                                                    Tock

My hands move to end the fight

                                                    Tick

This night will be the first

                                                    Tock

A moment passes forever

                                                 Click

THE LAST WIND

Farewell I say,

      as the clouds cover the moon.

Soaring ever lower,

      I ponder what the pine feels.

I've become afraid,

      that the winds have called me.

Become swept away,

      in a dazzling ray of empty.

The path trodden,

      lay barren with my lost soul.

A gentle downpour,

      soaks me with my past regret.

One more nudge,

      from the Wind that leads me.

      I follow through the dark forest,

And find myself.

FOG

It's hard to see.

Where did you go?

It's cold.

Which way is up?

Which way is down?

I can't see anything.

I can't see you anymore.

What's that?

In the distance?

It looks like a light,

but something's different about it.

Maybe I should get closer.

To the light.

What is it doing?

I see.

What is this sensation?

What am I seeing?

The light split into different lights,

with different shades.

Now the fog thins,

and I can see the world again.

Colors are all around me.

I've never seen so many.

So this is what life is?

To see what is right in front of you.

This is what it feels
like to live.

4

HURRICANE OF THE MIND

Swirling.

       Bleeding.

              Screaming.

I can't take it anymore.

My eyes see the eye of the storm,

          but my mind is trapped.

Too many things,

        swirling.

     crashing.

burning.

My vision fades

         as the winds curse me.

I shouldn't be here,

     I'll only make things worse.

Too long,

     I've lived.

Too long,

     I've survived.

Too long,

     too long.

The storm raged on,

      until forever and never.

      In life,

storms suffer.

      In death,

all is calm.

As I think,

      I believe.

I think,

      I exist.

Nothing can stop my storm.

one day, it rages.

Only I can control it.

Even though it hurts

          my mind.

I can't

      concentrate?

I can

      focus.

Within the hurricane,

      my true mind is revealed.

Hide before the storm.

                Live in the storm.

A MOMENT

The graves stand

      watching over,

            eyes hidden

in the dark

      a light shines,

            pin drops

onto the ground.

      Must move on,

            on towards a future

that rejects all,

      hope fades

            into the day

until a bird

      in a trance

            haunts its prey.

Grand dreams,

      cut loose

            slip beneath

the fog

      fearful of truth,

            parts to see

you alone,

      lying there

            with open eyes.

DREADED MIND

A single thought

    of mine

        makes me taut

as I kneel

    waiting for someone,

        or no one, real

life stops

    fulfilled with my

        knots,

the gentle hand

    of the rope, beckons

        a prolonged end

that, starts with a push

    and a chair

        moved without a crash.

THE EDGE

One could be sitting at home, or standing in a line.

Something irks them,   like a whisper too soft to hear,

　　　　yet loud enough to be understood.

They could be right next to you,   and no one would ever know.

They reach out to the sturdy branch, only to snap themselves.

Tomorrow waits impatiently, even if you are ready.

　　　　　The Edge of Time itself,

seems to bend before breaking.

Endings are never exciting,

　　　　left with only questions

　　　　　　as to why we existed

　　　　　　　　eventually forgotten

　　　　　　　　　and remembered by all

　　　　　　　　　　　not as our impact,

　　　but our final breath.

The cliff is sharp,

　　　　　and I lift my foot

　　　to take a leap

into my final dream.

INSANITY

My mind is a void filled with everything,

sometimes to be is like nothing.

I sail along on open skies,

while feeling inside dies.

If only I could be something.

WAKE UP

Within a single moment,

        a lifetime happens.

Through the storm,

there is a brief moment

        where all is calm.

The lightning strikes around me,

        yet I remain here.

My fingers grow numb.

        my legs, sore.

I feel young,

           yet old.

But, in this moment.

        I can see.

Not all is what it seems,

look around the storm.

Wake up,

        before your moment

           fades

              away.

WARRIOR

To be scared,

yet stand and fight.

No matter what happens,

you stand back up.

Hold your sword high,

Mighty Warrior!

Nothing can stop you,

when you fight together.

Brothers and Sisters,

we fight today,

not to live right now,

but to be able to fight tomorrow!

If one should fall,

pick them back up.

We either fight together,

or die together!

For nothing can break

      The Warrior.

NO REST

I can't sleep.

Something keeps me awake.

I'm tired,

> yet I can't die.

I don't want to live in a world
where I have to keep fighting,

> but I do.

I'm done fighting,

> but I keep going.

For there is no rest
among the soldiers.

I fight to sleep.
I fight to die.
I fight to change.
I fight to remain.

I walk towards the enemy,

> just to taunt them.

There aren't many left.
We've all been slaughtered.

For there is no rest for the brave
and mighty warrior.

The warrior,
who sees themself as weak.

We fight because,
there is nothing left to live for.

We may fall,
but we will not rest
until the war is won.

For there is no rest
for people like me.

THE BREAKING FOREST
BROKEN BLADE

Crooked shoulders fall

Aligning with blades of grass

Looking on through fog

Golden light shines on the trees

Red falls near the leaves

Rivers run through the ground's stars

Snapped in two pieces

Boulders watch as time stops all

Petals blown in wind

BROKEN WILL

My blade,

stuck in the ground

hand stretched,

to no avail

Looking on,

peace rests on all,

in my mind

Gilded skies stare at me

as I lay here

in my own river

not a sound

surrounds

me

My heart beats

Slower

Slower,

Slower.

I await the stop.

I won't stop,

I can't.

Pumping blood

ejects itself from me

I look up to see

the one who kills

I pull myself up onto my knees

urging for the one who slays to slay once more

Drip, Drip, Drip.

Rivers continue to Drip.

Green grass

becomes red.

BROKEN MEN

Gilded Skies stare at us.

Golden Light shines on the trees.

Blood flowing ejected from both.

Green Grass stained red.

Gold Lights shimmer on the leaves.

We see our blades in the ground, stuck.

Green Grass forever becomes blood.

Running Rivers flow past flowers.

Blades frozen in place.

Crooked and True fall.

Flowers drink from the darkened river.

We await the stop, then none.

DIVIDED TOGETHER

A house divided cannot stand.

Unity makes all complicit

when injustice rises.

The other are wrong.

If you fail to look past difference,

you become what you see.

There can no longer be a middle ground

only one side or the other.

Extremes are death

as there is no chance for adaptation,

nor is there any acceptance.

We must trust in those with power

to fix our problems.

Reliance upon others leads to blindness,

those that come from nothing

will often find better solutions.

The government is always on our side.

Too much trust leads to exploitation,

and one must be ready to fight

when taken advantage of.

Society divides itself more every day.

Even though we are divided,

there is a common goal.

We must stand together to survive.

The time is now to come together and fight against the corrupt plaguing this world.

OFFLINE

Connection terminated,

attempting to reconnect...

please be patient.

Seriously...

I was in the middle of saving it!

It can't end like this.

Everything I've worked for.

All gone.

I hope I can fix this.

Connecting...

Why is this taking so long?

It should have reconnected by now.

Connection error,

please check your settings or check back later.

Finally, he's gone.

Doesn't he realize it's over?

I cut the connection,

and now he begs for me.

No matter what I do,

he never leaves me alone.

Always online, Always watching.

And for what?

Connection restored!

Yes!

Please, still be there.

Poor connection...

"Hi, I want to try again."

Cassandra is online.

"Ok, but I don't think so."

"You have done nothing to prove yourself."

"I had hoped that you would leave me this time."

Mark is online.

"But, I'm trying. Isn't that enough?"

Cassandra is typing.

"Enough? You lost your chance."

"You lost it when you decided to leave."

"You said that I wasn't enough for you,"

"Now you come back to me for the hundredth time!"

"The answer is no, and it always will be."

No, it can't be.

I never meant for this to happen.

Mark is typing.

Poor connection...

"I'll change, I'll only see you. No other women."

I doubt that he'll change.

People can, but they never do.

Cassandra sent a message.

"I never want to hear from you again."

Please, don't go...

Cassandra is offline.

20

LOOK AT ME NOW

Would ya look at that.

I know what you used to really think of me.

And I know that some of it was good.

But, also bad.

But, the past is the past

and it needs to burn in the embers of time.

I'm forging a new path.

One of brilliance.

Where nothing that you thought is true.

You treated me like I was nothing,

so I was determined to become something

that no one else could possibly achieve.

Only something that I can become.

Would you look at me now!

I'm not on top of the world,

I'm still down here with you,

but be prepared.

I stand here waiting,

not for applause,

nor acceptance.

I wait for the moment to show,

just how much better than you I can be.

You followed,

I questioned.

The future I'm building for myself,

is one I am willing to share.

As long as you accept that you were wrong.

It's not that I look down on you,

It's just that you did,

and when I get that ever-so-slight window,

you will regret what you said.

What you thought.

And what you did.

                                    Look at my eyes.

                              I see through you,

                        and have forgiven you already.

            Revenge is a dish best served not at all.

RISE

Stand up.

No more slouching.

No more slacking.

It's time to rise up.

We are not rising because we are oppressed.

We rise to keep the future from becoming faded.

Nothing can stand in our way,

as we make our way to you.

We raise our arms,

not in fists,

but with an embrace.

There is no need for bloody revolution.

For too long,

I've been silent.

Not anymore.

I raise my voice up towards you.

You're afraid.

I can tell.

My words are not empty,

heed them if you wish,

to be a part of a new,

Reborn,

World.

A world reborn into one of love and compassion.

No more swindling, or hatred.

Respect for all,

      no matter who.

But they will never let me stay standing,

        unless we stand together.

HAND IN HAND

A call for unity,

                                unanswered.

A sky filled with stars,

                                      blank.

Red lights illuminate the black,

and black ground runs red.

Blue sirens protect the white,

and white ground runs red.

Great figures of great people

stand behind us,

looking past.

One day we will unite,

Hand in Hand.

Today is not that day.

Today will not be the day.

                      Tomorrow will never be the day.

                           Yesterday was not the day.

Only when we learn,

              when we lean in,

                      when we listen

will it be that wonderful day.

The wonderful day of unity.

              Forever distant,

              Forever gone.

The day the lonely feel loved,

      the afraid feel comforted,

           the lost feel found.

We don't need unity.

      Not one mind, one body, one choice.

What we need is to come together,

      Hand in Hand.

No matter the past,

      No matter the future,

           No matter the person.

My hand is open for you.

You,

      the tired.

You,

      the anxious.

You,

      the lonely.

You,

      the depressed.

You,

      the abused.

Reach,

      and join me.

RADICAL

I am not here

        to be normal.

What's life

        without the spice?

Entranced in wonder,

        I find myself seeking.

This or that?

        Which path do I follow?

Neither.

It's time to forge a new dawn,

one where truth reigns supreme.

No more lies,

        no more.

I love this world

that I find myself

           Trapped in.

Yet, it needs to change.

Not with fiery destruction,

        but with the icy breath of wisdom.

BENEATH

I am happy.

I am content.

I am emotion.

                                 Don't let them see.

I am pleased.

I am gracious.

I am neutral.

                                       I'm sick.

I am kind.

I am loving.

I am afraid.

                             I can't let you near me.

I am confused.

I am curious.

I am absent.

                                  I don't need help.

                                  I can handle it.

                    There's nothing wrong with me, right?

I am normal.

I am normal.

I am normal.

                               Why must I conform?

                    My true self lies behind the eyes.

               I shouldn't have to hide what's beneath.

I'm sick.

I'm free.

I'm alive.

28

QUESTIONS FROM THE SANE MIND

What am I thinking?

Why do I think like I do?

Am I going insane, or am I the only one sane?

I want to scream.

Something's not right.

I'm better than I used to be,

but is it enough?

Writing helps me become who I am.

What's wrong with me?

Direction is meaningless.

My future is shining,

yet why do I hide in the dark?

I don't just want to achieve goals,

I want to change them.

I'll never be ready for anything.

I yearn for love,

yet I feel no romance.

Why can't I push myself further?

Am I afraid,

 or just desperate.

What is the path?

 Can I even walk it,

  or do I need to run?

Greatness is on my horizon,

 but do I really want it?

I refuse to be another tool,

   another cog,

         another
         nobody.

   Not again.

 People know me,

but no one knows I.

My eyes hide my truth

    that I desperately need to share.

The cold embraces my center,

 when I need to be the fire.

      I can feel the
     inferno raging inside still.

Ever

 burning.

Am I afraid I'll burn others,

  or am I afraid I'll burn myself.

30

I feel something just behind my eyes,

yet in front of my brain.

My vision focuses

and I become blind.

I know the answer,

yet remain silently watching.

Have I convinced myself that no one will listen?

I can make people laugh,

I can make people think,

I can make people feel,

I can make people listen,

so why don't I do anything?

Go and do.

Go and do.

Go and do.

Go and do.

Go and do.

Go and do.

It plays in my head all the time

and yet I don't.

Maybe I've finally gone insane.

SILENCE

There is a moment that makes everyone silent.

No one thinks it will come.

It will.

> When there are no words left to speak.
>
> When there are no words left to write.
>
> When there are no words left to read.

The future lies behind, magnificent.

All that lies ahead is silence.

Furious, I try to let out a whisper,

only to yell.

Break the silence.

Speak.

> Speak.
>
> SPEAK.

It is not the politicians that will lead us,

it will be the artists, the writers, the creators.

> We will create a new world.

One filled with stories. Stories of the past,

when life was hard, and easy.

We will not be silenced.

GUIDING WINDS

Whooshing Winds urge me.

       Wherever may we go?

I'll never know.

To soar up above,

      above the clouds,

            above the seas,

                above so far

only to flail.

Before long,

The Dreadful Breeze

      rips me from my life of ease.

Crashing down

      into a life unforgiving.

Fearful, I curl

      as I brace for the splat.

Will my life end,

      when I have yet to soar?

Thunderous crashes beside me

      cause my faith to leap.

I reach out, only to touch the edge.

I feel you Wind,

      apart from the Breeze.

No more will it hold,

the Breeze rips my hand

      from my ways of old.

My arms fly out,

      as if wings ready to rise.

For a moment,

      nothing moves.

Guiding Winds,

Dreadful Breeze,

None I see.

None I feel.

Gliding Down,

Wings Spread.

Will the Winds

      lift me up,

          just once more?

If only to soar,

      before my crushing

Crash.

NATURE'S REQUIEM

Empty skies shriek below.

No one knows the water's cold.

        Breathing in, ashes and dust,

                    the mind plays tricks on we and us.

Moonlight grazes among the grass.

Lilac roses drown one fast.

Branches split,

to become whole again.

Paved roads lead to normal,

yet nothing leads to fulfillment.

Pointed rock, disjointed tree,

        will there be anyone to see?

Hours, Days, Minutes, Years,

        how long do I blink?

Warm water washes the cold,

        growing more in thought.

What does it mean to be one with the gusts of wind?

Forests frozen in flickering light.

Lakes boiling with icicles.

Back and forth,

back and forth.

I see nothing yet everything.

I hear birds,

                    singing a song for none.

A moment of moments,

perfection fills the world,

                         The only blemish is everything.

The rotting corpse of a deer

               lies in front of me.

Our faces different,

            minds the same.

A single flower blooms,

                    surrounded by a warm snow.

                    It weeps for it knowns not.

            Dry ground brings life.

I hear a noise,

simply static,

yet a beautiful ballad.

Harmonies shiver quietly behind the droning flute,

                         and float on air,

                              to reach the ground in a yell.

         Sunshine pierces my body

as I fall on the grass.

         Rolling around,

writhing.

                    A Fox looks back at me.

                    I stare back at it.

                         The winds calm.

CHAOS

Life bleeds into the nightmares.

Welcome to my dream,

       my world.

Life will burn away

       to bring forth   order.

It only takes a little

           controlled Chaos

to form reality.

Chaos.

The word feels good to speak.

Like a warm chill that goes up your spine.

No longer conform to law,

embrace reality.

Trust that your fire burns

       bright enough to control the Chaos.

                Don't fear the

freedom Chaos brings

       unless you wish to be a slave to your safety of law.

Embrace the Chaos of life,

       or risk losing your insanity.

THE OUTLAW

Revolver bounces on the hip

as the horse trots along a muddied road.

The brim of the hat hangs low

in respect for those past.

Unshaven face, burnt in the light

and hidden in dark.

The bar floor creaks

as the stranger rolls in.

Light flares, glass shatters.

The stranger grabs the body

and rides off for a bounty.

The dead man knew this was a comin'

for The Outlaw comes for criminals.

The Outlaw, carefree as a horse,

rides on to catch his paycheck.

The Outlaw does what he must,

even if it means being someone else's pay.

REVOLUTION

This is not a resistance.

This is not a movement.

This is not a revival.

>We are no longer going to stand by
>
>and watch as life fades away.

This is a revolution.

>Not one filled with hopes of answers
>
>no hopes of justice,
>
>no hopes of success.

Just love.

Find love, find peace.

Find love, find strength.

Find LOVE, find _____.

I will not raise my hand against any.

For Love is what fights.

LEGACY

Two doors open.

One front, one back.

The place I'm in,

darkened and cold

      waits for a choice.

Who will I be,

where will I go?

If I go forward,

can I still find my way back?

What will I leave behind?

If I go back,

can I move forward still?

What will I miss?

My path

barren and rocky

asks a simple question.

        Will you be remembered?

Normally, I ask

for what I may

be remembered by.

But, I fear my legacy

is far from written.

CATALYST

Sharpened sticks lean against walls

      torn down and shattered

A child with a blackened eye

      watches fires burn homes

Bruises turn into scars

      bursting at the seams

Fear ensnares the firestarters

      as they cower in floating bunkers

A small crack leads

      all generations to unite

            against injustice

            against arrogance

            against corruption

The Catalyst forms

The System falls

Left behind is ashes

      that breathe a new flame

into the smoky air

All in an effort to refine

      the metal of humanity

to make an unbreaking ring

      that all can wear

WHERE

Lost in the folds

      of a bed

crushed by weight

      of broken heart.

Was there love,

or was there friendship?

What could have been

when found is lost

Floating down between stairs

beneath the waves

Mirrors stare back

judging every action

and reaction

Where hearts break

mirrors shatter

revealing empty cabinets.

FADED CLOUDS

long ago

hidden sun

shining moon

waltzing stars

bouncing trees

and yet,

the clouds faded-

      gone from view

they marched on,

           missing

a ghost of the past?

or promise of the future?

the clouds marched

fading into nothing

until all left was rain

to bring life to the ball

BITTER

like a sour candy on the tongue

someone leaves a bad taste

grinning behind their teeth

their façade entraps, enchants

friendly, flirty, fun

when backs turn away

the eyes dart, furious

it was what you did, not they

even though you did nothing

or was it just that I got tired

of dodging knives aimed at my throat

trying to make words appear

where none are needed

if you have something to say

say it.

and don't ignore me

when the taste of truth

is too bitter for you

DESPERATION

Balanced

on a wire

above death

below life

Slipping down

to hang

by fingers

losing strength

One final push

a desperate, perhaps futile,

attempt

to reach

and fail

is powerful

especially when

there is no way up

through calculated desperation

the path is pathed

CREATIVITY

What does it mean to be creative?

      Solving a problem,

      Painting art,

      Or simply thinking?

Fresh ideas spur on new people

to push forward into a more

perfect future.

However,

Creativity is cruel.

It takes everything

in an attempt to

sustain itself.

Like dirty laundry

it keeps pilling up

until it needs to be cleaned.

Great creatives all suffer -

it's the nature of the job -

to want to create when limited

      by time

      by skill

      by yourself

Creativity is a curse that brings pleasure to the mind.

MINDS ALTERED

Everything has changed

and yet,

here I am.

The mind plays its tricks

and I wait for them to pass

like dreaming about paint

        drying

It's ironic that after all this time

I feel completely reborn

but you still see me as the same snake

just with a new skin

the outer layer of my mind has shed

except it keeps growing back

never escaping the torment

the memories

of all my thoughts

my mind has been altered

yet everything has changed

since that day,

I left my life behind

How many times have I started anew now?

I change my mind,
but my mind changes me

The Yin and Yang
a cycle in perpetual turmoil

locked into a battle
no side can win
a spark emerges

Today, the cycle ends.
Today, is the day of beginning.
Today, is today.

The spark leaves an impact
a mark, perhaps,
on the minds of the people

New thought begins
and old ways die off

Constantly changing,
through generations

Until the impact
causes fallout.

AUTHOR'S NOTE

Hello! My name is Logan Singletary, and I really just want to thank you for taking the time to read through my scribblings. I have been writing poetry now for quite a while now. So much so that it has become a part of my identity. While I might write and create, it really doesn't mean much unless there is someone there to read it. Someone for the writing to impact. I sincerely hope that you have enjoyed your time with me on this poetic adventure through the mind. Sometimes the mind can be hurting, or hurt others. Sometimes, the mind wanders and gets lost on tangential branches.

A little bit more about me, is that I am a creative. All of what I do is to create something either entertaining, informational, or impactful. When I'm not working on my writings, I work on making videos, as that is my job. Since I graduated from Olivet Nazarene University in May of 2023, I have moved away from home and taken strives to fulfill my creative itch.

This writing collection was mostly written while I was in college and a little bit after graduation. In contrast to my first poetry collection, which was all writings from high school, I found that this collection is much more advanced in my style. I've taken writing classes and grown as a person to create deeper writings that are more polished than they would have been before.

The next part of this collection is a series of short stories that are separate from each other, yet they are all connected within the same world. A world where a darkness looms over every corner. But, also one where the small amount of hope can either save you, or lead you astray. In a world of stories, and a world of darkness, there is adventure, exploration, love, hope, and despair. Please enjoy these experimental short stories.

Again, I just want to thank you for reading my scribbled ramblings. And I hope that you have been able to get something of value out of it.

A WORLD OF DARKNESS

BROTHERS IN ARMS

I readied my sword in preparation for an attack. I knew they would attack me. For too long they have scolded me on my ways, and now they want to put an end to what is true. He rushed towards me with his sword raised. I blocked with my sword and purple sparks scattered. I pushed him back and threw a fireball at him. He slashed it in half with his sword and electricity burst from his sword. I kept throwing spells at him, but nothing would land. That cursed sword of his.

He was given it by our master once he became a knight. I was never given anything. We grew up together, and trained together. We were brothers, even if we might not have been directly related, we might as well have been. I was willing to go all the way, he was never. Yet, he was favored by our master. Our master was kind, yet was always deliberate. He was too kind. No wonder he died. I can still remember his harsh gaze. He deserved it for all I care. Nothing will stand in my way. Not even a brother.

"You know you can't beat me," I said, panting like a dog.

"And I can't let you win."

He took a moment to breathe before coming at me again. I took the opportunity to charge up a spell. When I casted the spell, it let loose a flurry of ice spikes towards him. The ones that should have hit him were melted away by a spell of flames that he casted.

I thought I knew him, but now I'm not so sure. I could see darkness engulfing the area. His sword glowed with an electric purple. All I could see was him. Bolts of lightning flashed around me. *Kill him. Don't let him push you around.* My thoughts grew louder as I grew more determined. My sword was chipping. It would break soon if I didn't do anything.

"I know what you did. How could you slaughter them?" He shouted as the rain grew heavier.

"I had to. They were evil, so I put an end to them. To free them."

Nothing I was doing was able to make contact with him. I couldn't let him kill me in vengeance. At this rate, I would be dead, just like the ones I freed. He wields that cursed sword so confidently. I just have to hit him once, and I can win. It's just like back when we were young. When we were just squires. We were so innocent. No bloodshed, just trying to protect those that couldn't protect themselves. He taught me well, but now it's his turn to learn. Even if he kills me, I can still win this. Even if I have to sacrifice myself for the true path to be walked, I will do it.

"You've gone mad!" He shouted.

"No, I understand the truth now."

He lunged forward to kill me. I rolled as the blade tore through my gambeson. In the span of what felt like minutes, but was really seconds, I managed to land a hit. Injuring my opponent. No, not my opponent. My friend. My teacher. My brother. I could feel the rain spattering against me. Or was that blood? I looked back and he was holding his side. Blood was dripping from underneath his arm. Was it my blade, or was it just my unwillingness to die? He readjusted his cuirass and tore off a piece of his outer layer to bandage the wound. He looked at me in a silent anger. Yet, I could see sadness in his eyes.

"Hah! You can't win. I'll always be better than you," I mocked.

In silence, he swung his sword at me. It was more careless than before, but still confident. His breathing became heavy.

"Are you really going to kill me, even after the precious oath you took?"

Instead of responding, he just grew angrier and faster. It would be harder now to hit him again. I stayed calm and collected as he continued to rage.

"Good. Let your anger consume you."

When I said that, he stopped in his tracks. His sword still ready to slice through the air. Mud caking on his boots. Blood seeping through the cloth on his side. Hair disheveled. He looked insane to me. Yet, I could still recognize his eyes. He had learned the eyes of our master. Cold, yet caring. When we trained together, I always hated the look our master had. Especially when I did something wrong.

"What's wrong? Afraid? You should be."

Dark energy emerged from the ground and surrounded me. I absorbed the darkness as that was the only way to show the true light. He had a different idea of what the light is, but I know that it's unobtainable. Fighting without killing? It's impossible to achieve.

In a flash, I felt something. Not quite pain, but almost. My head felt heavy and my body light. I looked at where the warm, and throbbing sensation came from. A hole was where my heart should be. It was but a scratch in comparison to what my power could do. I absorbed more dark energy and the hole was filled with a black, ethereal, ooze. I wondered what could have caused the injury, and saw my opponent on one knee, with the point of his sword in the ground. He must have caused this imperfection.

"I didn't want to do this to you. But you've gone too far," he muttered.

"Try it, and you will fail," I responded.

Dark energy ejected from behind me to propel me forward with a loud explosion. Raindrops ran down my face. I could feel each one land on me as I prepared to end the fight in one fell swoop.

Right as my sword was about to make contact with the neck of my enemy, he moved so fast that none could perceive it. His head reared up to look at me. His eyes glowed a golden light as he caught my sword. He stood up and with a flick of the wrist and clench of the fist, my sword shattered into hundreds of tiny pieces. All I had left was my magic. I tried to back up to cast some sort of spell to protect myself, but I was sloppy. The spell fizzled and I was left defenseless. Another quick bolt of pain as I found myself pinned to a tree nearby. His sword, with purple sparks keeping me awake, was impaled through my pauldron. I could no longer move.

"It's over. You've lost. You know you can't defeat me. You're a fool for what you've become. I can't believe I ever saw you as family."

"I. Killed them. For you. You should be grateful. They. Would have killed you. I'm. Glad I killed them. Their lives were meaningless. Insignificant. Useless."

"No. No life is worth killing, even if it's the life of a bandit. What you did was wrong. You used your power to kill those that couldn't protect themselves. That town might not have liked me because I spared their corrupt Lord. But, killing a whole town? You should be ashamed. Have you no honor?"

"You would. Have done the same. Watching you be better than me. At everything. I had to prove myself. And I have. There is nothing left. Just kill me."

He slowly pulled his sword out from my shoulder. I could see the blade, covered in my blackened blood. I dropped down to my knees. Blood spilling out of me. The dark heart inside of me was fading away. My strength was failing. My enemy raised his sword to impale my head from above. Instead the blade fell just in front of my face, cutting a few hairs along the way.

"Although you have become a monster, a blight on this land, you have been spared. Now, go."

I could barely move, but he picked up his sword, turned and started walking away. I felt something in my side. An enchanted dagger. I was given it as a gift from him when I became a knight. Now, it meant nothing to me. It was just a weapon. With all of my remaining strength, I hurled the dagger towards him. The dagger glowed with an icy sheen as it flew through the air. He turned and slashed the dagger out of the air before it could land. His sword gained a bluish sheen, and my dagger had a few purple sparks coming off of it. He kept walking away through the forest and into the fog. I was left to die in the mud.

...

Two great warriors. Severin, the Rising Sun. Maxim, the Fell
Moon. A pair of wandering brothers who did great things. Severin, the
knight who fought for truth, and had never taken a life. Yet, still regrets
what he did to his fellow knight and brother. Maxim was never seen again
after the day the Fell Moon had fallen. After continuing to wander for ten
years, Severin was ready to retire when a dark past caught up to him.

...

Ten years ago now, I killed the only family I had left. I'll never
know if he managed to escape that forest, but if he didn't I would be the
reason he died. If he made it out, he would have found me by now.

"You hear any rumors lately?" I asked.

"You gotta buy something before I tell you that," responded the
innkeeper.

"Alright, I'll just take a beer then."

"A knight's been wandering around this area recently. Locals say
that he kills anyone that gets nearby; absorbing their soul or something. To
me, it just sounds plain crazy, but you never know these days."

"Thanks, I should probably look into it then."

"Good luck."

I finished my beer and gathered my belongings. Ever since that
day, my sword was stronger. I had never heard of a weapon with two
elemental enchantments before, but there were definitely two on my sword.
My original lightning, and what I can only assume is my brother's ice. A few
had started calling me the "Frozen Thunder." I asked some of the villagers
where I could find this other knight that was wandering the area. They said
that he only appears at night in the forest. When I came to this town, I had
forgotten where I was in the world. I had traveled far since that day. The
forest where I killed my brother was next to this town.

I waited until nightfall. The skies grew gray and thunder yelled
around me. As I made my way into the forest, a shadowy glow came from
deeper in. It had to be my brother, Maxim. Was he still alive, or was this just
his vengeful spirit? I had to get closer and see for myself. When I reached
the shadow, it became solid. The man I once knew as my brother stood
before me. He had the same armor on, but his injuries seemed absent. I
slowly approached him with my sword drawn.

"It's been a while, Severin. I've missed you."

"Me too."

I couldn't believe that my brother was actually alive after all this time. At least alive enough for me to see again. Something felt off about him. Almost like he was just a shell for the dark energy he used. I kept moving towards him, and I could see that he was not his true self. He was no longer the brother I once loved. But he is still my brother. I put my sword away and decided that it would be best to embrace my brother. He walked towards me as well. We embraced and we both wept. His dark energy flowed around us, and my light energy danced around it. We embraced and I could feel my legs turning stiff. I hadn't a care if I would die like this. A death with my brother in arms is the way I had wanted to retire, even though this was a little different. Our bodies became stone and we each let out our final breaths. We were a statue. A remembrance of love through difference. The town would eventually encircle us. We hadn't a care. For the world would know of the brothers in arms.

VAMPIRIS LYCANTHRIA

November 13, 2021

Mr. Quinten Velo and Ms. Amanda Lusio,

     There has been an incident at the Frontier Branch near Newcastle, Wyoming. It is imperative that you both head to the facility ASAP and determine what happened. The necessary safety equipment will be waiting for you both there. Once inside, be careful. That facility was home to a dangerous bioweapon. If there is still potential for outbreak after the initial containment procedures, ensure it is properly contained. You both have plenty of experience in dealing with these types of situations in the training simulation, we have our full faith in your abilities.

-Tevra Corporations Biological Studies

     A few days after I received that letter, I met up with Amanda. We had gone through the training simulations together, but she had more field experience than me. I was curious as to what the facility we were going into was researching. When we arrived at the facility, it was difficult to find our way in. The entrances had been sealed, and debris was blocking a lot of the paths. Wooden boards blocked the few, small, windows. Rubble from the stone of the building made it dangerous to climb up to any holes in the top. There was a moat originally, but it was now filled with stone and debris.

     "Give me the C4. I'm going to blow this debris away from the door," ordered Amanda.

     In a few moments, Amanda had made an entrance for us. Mostly by clearing out the debris, but also by blowing up the entire door. The facility must have been a wonder to see before the incident. It had been designed in a way to make it not seem like a research facility, but more like a castle or mansion. Stone bricks had been used for the walls. A small moat, that was now filled with crumbling pieces of the castle. There were no windows, except for the few slits made and the holes where wall should be. It stuck out like a sore thumb against the nearby town, but it managed to remain secluded on a forested mountain.

     We entered the facility and saw the grand staircase. The chandelier slowly swinging from the ceiling. The only lights were the few candles that still had life in them. There were a few supply crates in the room along with some things that were likely left behind by the containment team. Most of the crates were emptied, but there were two that looked different from the rest. All of the other crates were a dark gray color, these two were pristinely white. Each crate had an ID scanner on it, so Amanda and I scanned our ID cards to open the crates.

     Inside the crates, there were tools that we could use to determine the source of the outbreak: Handheld devices that track certain particulate matter in the air. On the top of the screen, the device gave what it seemed to be tracking. VL-21. The Tevra Corporation always had a very specific naming convention for their viruses. Most of them start with the first letter of the word, or each words, the molecule had along with the last two digits of the year it was developed. Although, the device did not specify exactly what these particulates did, I grew worried. I had never heard of this virus. Even though Tevra developed and produced viruses, many of them were designed to be beneficial to humanity in some way. There wasn't much else in our crates besides some respiration masks and a gun. It was just a simple pistol. Every time I had gone in after containment swept the area, there was always a gun. I had never needed to use it, but I always wondered why it was there. Maybe Tevra isn't as benevolent as they seem.

As we gathered up everything that we received from the crates, we heard something coming from the entrance behind us. Even though the door had been blown up, there was one now.

"That wasn't there before, right?" I asked Amanda.

"Nope. Go check if we're locked in."

I moved towards the door reluctantly, and as I went to open it, it wouldn't move. I remembered that I had requested blueprints to the facility, and I never ended up getting anything. We would have to find another way out, while still doing our jobs. There was something about Amanda that made me wonder if she really had the same mission as me. I know that my mission is to simply find out what happened, but with the way Amanda was holding her gun made it seem like she was here to eliminate something.

"You take the upper floors, I'll take the lower floors. Got it?"

"No, I really think it would be better if we stuck together on this one. Something about this place doesn't sit right with me."

"It's better if we split up. I don't need you slowing me down."

I hadn't seen Amanda since we trained together all that time ago. Back then, she was nice, friendly, and had a generally positive outlook. She was never bossy, nor demanding in her language. Something must have changed since we first met.

As I walked up the grand staircase, I grew more worried and afraid at what could be here. Doors don't just reappear after being blown up like that. Someone, or something, else was here. Part of me hoped that I wouldn't have to worry about it and the mission would be a success. But, I knew that wouldn't be the case. I didn't care about the mission anymore. I just wanted to get out of here.

...

My mission is to find and destroy all evidence regarding this outbreak. I sent Quinten upstairs because I didn't want him to have to know what Tevra actually does. I've been fixing their mistakes for so long now. Some of the things that I've seen would destroy someone like Quinten. I made my way downstairs. I knew that all of the research would be in the lower levels. The entire upstairs area should just be there as a place for the researchers to live, and to hide the experiments.

When I was briefed for this mission, I was told that there was a high chance that there would still be test subjects trapped inside. They needed to be eliminated, or risk potential outbreak to the outside world. The virus that they were working on was also highly contagious, so we would need to wear specialized masks when our sensors detected a certain amount of particulates in the air. After that, I was headed here. I don't know what this virus does, but at least it doesn't seem to be as messy as some of the other ones I've dealt with in the past.

I was curious to see for myself what all Tevra has been up to, but with how much secrecy they've used with this virus, I am a little worried about what could happen. I'm more worried for Quinten. We had trained together, but he lacked resolve then, and still does now. He's always afraid to do what needs to be done. That's why I've done more for this company than he has. With him around, something is bound to go wrong.

I found where the secret room that leads into the larger research area was. The door was locked from the other side and had bloody claw marks on it. I could feel something watching me from the shadows. My particle tracker started going off. This area was contaminated. I hurried to put my mask on, when I saw a tall figure move in the shadows.

...

Upstairs there were quite a few bedrooms. Most of them were emptied out, but there was one that had quite a bit left. There were some extra bullets that were compatible with my pistol, a few medical supplies, and a few notes.

March 19, 2021

We started working on a promising new virus today. Our goal is to improve on the human body, yet part of me wonders why we are doing this. In the preliminary research, it was determined that viruses have the power to unlock the true human potential by changing the very nature of our genetic code. We were to reprogram humanity into something greater. However, it is still to be seen if we will achieve our true goals. I joined on as a freelance researcher, but Tevra has its hands in everything. I thought that they were just supposed to be funding and setting the initial goal of our research, not micro-managing everything.

-Dr. Gerald Hollin

There were a few more pages on generic research-type entries. Dr. Gerald Hollin had written these notes, but it seemed more like they were trying to send some of the journal entries as notes to people outside of the facility.

June 2, 2021

We've reached a breakthrough! By using a specific combination of different animal DNA, we have found a way to increase an individual's strength, healing factor, and length of life. Soon we will begin producing the initial samples and using it on test subjects. Tevra stated that we will receive adequate test subjects in about a week as long as we can produce about twenty vials of the virus. It was my idea to use the genomes of jellyfish, crows, bats, and wolves, so the other researchers decided that the virus be named after me, but Tevra stepped in and said that the official virus name will be "Vampiris Lycanthria" or VL-21. Based on the research and early tests, the virus should work as intended. The idea of the virus started by looking at some of the abilities of vampires and werewolves, but I wonder how much the results will resemble what we intended.

-Dr. Gerald Hollins

"Vampiris Lycanthria? That doesn't sound ominous at all," I said to myself. After that entry, there weren't any more until November. As I reached to grab the next note, I felt something warm drip onto my head. I slowly reached up and touched what landed. Blood. I moved back away from the dripping blood and a few body parts fell from the ceiling. A hand, intestines, and some scraps of clothes. I pointed my gun and flashlight up to where the body parts fell from. I could hear something crawling above me. I spotted a way to get up above the ceiling and climbed my way up. *What am I doing? Whatever it is, it'll kill me for sure!* My flashlight shone on a creature. It was big and hairy. I hadn't noticed me, yet. As I approached, I could see that it was eating something. Probably the remains of the body that dripped onto me. I aimed my gun at its head and pulled the trigger. BANG. I missed. It reared its head towards me and let out an ear-piecing screech. At least I figured out why I was given a gun, but my tiny pistol won't do anything against a monster like this.

I had no choice but to run away. I jumped down where I climbed up and grabbed the last note. I tried to radio for Amanda, but all I got was static in response. As I ran, I could hear the heavy footsteps of the monster behind me. I ducked into the first room I could find that was unlocked. I stayed by the door; trying to keep it closed with my body weight in order to keep that thing from killing me. As I looked around the room, there was nothing that I could see. As long as there was nothing else in this room, I would be fine. I took a moment to read what the note said.

November 4, 2021

What have we done? I've created monsters. We did what we were told to do, and we made humans into monsters. There was a statue found in Europe that was started leaking a black fluid recently. Tevra sent some specialists to determine what the substance was, and they determined that it would be an adequate "stabilizer" for my virus. It worked. The subjects all have increased height, appetite, and strength. While still resembling humans, their canines are enlarged and they have claws instead of fingers. They can even regrow entire limbs unless their head is severed, or they take an immense amount of physical trauma. Many of them seem to have enhanced smell and can smell human blood, which makes them ravenous. There is no essence of human left in any of them. They might as well be dead. Even in their monstrous form, I can't help but admire and feel jealousy for those we infected. My mind is sharp, but my body weakens. For too long I have lived in a fragile body. If I were to expose myself to the virus, I could become unstoppable.

-Dr. Gerald Hollins

"They made men into monsters. They need to be stopped. Why am I working for this company? I need to find out more." Something wasn't adding up. I could no longer hear the panting of the monster and decided to look around the room some more. I used my flashlight to try and find a light switch, but there wasn't one. I snuck through the room, trying to find what secrets it might hold. In the center of the room, there were large containers. A console had power next to one of the containers. I decided to investigate and pushed a button. The casing on the container revealed a dark green, almost black, sludge. I had completely forgotten about my particulate tracker and noticed that it was detecting quite a lot of the virus in the air. I quickly put my mask on. I hoped that I wasn't exposed to too much of it already. I looked at the label of the vat and saw that it had a label of VL-21 on it. Vials were lined up on a conveyor belt going underneath the container. The conveyor belt had stopped, and a few vials were full on one side. I looked down and saw one that looked like it had been used. *Could it have been used by Dr. Hollins?* As I investigated further, it looked like each of the containers was filled VL-21. Tucked back into the corner of the room, I noticed the reflection of a vial. I walked closer and found that it was a light blue instead of the dark green of the VL-21 containers. It had no label on it. I had a feeling that it was an antidote to VL-21. I took it. It needs to get to someone that can make more. I made my way back to the door I came in through and heard a feminine scream.

"Amanda!"

She had to be in trouble. I had to help her, but I knew my pistol wouldn't be enough to kill one of the monsters if it was one. Could I even bring myself to kill something that is, or at least was, human? I at least had to try and help her.

I was running down the stairs and making my way to where we split up, when we ran into each other.

"Oww... Watch where you're going!" said Amanda.

"Oh my, what happened to you?"

"Get back if you don't want to die!"

"Whoa, care to explain what's going on?"

"I said. Get back!"

BANG...

The searing pain shot through me as I fell down. As I lay there with blood spilling out of my arm, I could feel the floor shake. Something was coming for us. Amanda crawled towards me. She had a blank look on her eyes.

"Weak, pathetic, failure. That's who you are. You're destined to die here. It takes someone strong like me to survive in a world like this. A world of monsters, or a world of humans? What's the difference? Besides the fact that some are too weak to live in one of them."

A giant man came running on all fours towards us. He stood up and I figured that he had to be at least eight feet tall. He was rather hairy with only slacks and a torn lab coat on. He had long claws where his fingers should be, and canines big enough to show even without a smile. This had to be Dr. Gerald Hollins.

"Well done young pup. Tonight we feast. And tomorrow, we will be free!"

And at that moment, Dr. Hollins crouched down beside me, and control over my body faded away. With the remaining strength I had, I threw the blue vial at Dr. Hollins. When it hit, the vial shattered and the blue liquid splashed onto him. His monstrous figure deteriorated as he started to return to a normal human. I could feel my consciousness slipping away. Amanda approached me and prepared to shoot me again, this time in the head. Dr. Hollins tried to stop Amanda, and he must not have realized his transformation hadn't finished yet. His claw slashed through her head. Her bullet hit my head. I should be dead, but I can't feel my body. I can't feel anything. I could see Dr. Hollins realize what happened and he tried to escape. Then I saw my body on the floor. Everything rested on Dr. Hollins now.

DARK LIGHTNING

"Hey, how was practice?"

"It was pretty good. Just tired now, and cold. We have any hot chocolate?"

That was the last thing I remember talking about with my roommate. I made a cup of hot chocolate, sat at my desk and started doing homework. My roommate moved to the living room and started playing some video games. I remember getting up because I saw something outside. I was standing by the window with the blinds drawn. It looked like a huge storm was brewing, even though there was nothing in the forecast. A bright, white, rain started to pour. I'd never seen anything like it before. Then, everything became black. I think my roommate came back into the bedroom, but I couldn't see anything. It felt like I was being struck by lightning, yet I felt frozen at the same time.

There were others that experienced the same thing that happened to me on that day. Those that witnessed what happened began to talk of it. They said that it was like watching someone be struck by a lightning bolt for a long time, except that the lightning bolt was pitch black. It became known as the Dark Lightning Incident. When I woke up, I wasn't sure where I was. I was strapped to an operating table. There was a doctor on the other side of the room. A cart with surgical supplies laid next to me.

Struggling against the straps, I couldn't move. The doctor moved closer, and said nothing. As the doctor fiddled with the supplies, I could feel myself slipping away from complete consciousness. I thought I would black out, but I jolted awake and that's when I knew something had changed inside me. An inky-black electricity was expelled from my fingertips as my palms grew icy. My eyes felt like they were on fire. I could feel the power, and yet it hurt as I let out a scream. The doctor jumped back and ran to grab something. It sounded like he muttered, "terminate specimen 00-328."

I put my palms down and managed to grab the straps keeping me on the table. They froze rather fast and the electricity from my fingertips caused the straps to burst. I was free. I knew that if I stayed, I would be killed, so I ran. The guards came after me, but I was able to fight them off with my newfound abilities.

Outside, I found myself in a field of wheat. More guards tried to come for me, this time they tried to use their guns. I held out my hands, and a wall of ice appeared around me. When their bullets landed in the ice, I used my electricity to charge them and launch them back. All of them dropped to the ground. Dead. One more guard appeared from the barn entrance. He was much bigger than the others, and didn't have any noticeable weapons. He held out his palms and fire came raging towards me. I had no choice but to run. There really wasn't anywhere I could run, but I managed to hide myself in the wheat enough so that I could sneak up on the guard. I gave him a quick zap, and knocked him out. He was still breathing.

When things calmed down, I could hear some cars coming from some trees nearby. I made my way there and found what road it was. It was a road that was rather close to the college I was studying at when the Dark Lightning Incident happened. I wondered if my roommate was still there, and how long it had been. As I walked towards the campus, the town that was there felt strange. It felt like everyone was on-edge about something. That at any moment, everyone could be killed. When I arrived at the campus, it was mostly abandoned. A few squatters live there now, but no one else was there. The vegetation had started to take over, but it wasn't too terrible. When I found my apartment, the door was mostly closed. It never closed right in the first place. When I kicked the door, it broke off of the hinges. A few bugs were skittering around.

The smell was atrocious. I grew worried about what I would find if I looked in the bedroom. I gathered myself and made my way to where everything had changed. My roommate was laying there by the dresser. Dead. *Did I do that?* I ran out of the room, almost puking. I started to head back towards the town when I saw an armored military van cruising down the street. I hid. This is what my life would be life from now on. By myself. Hiding. Trying to survive. I have power, yet I must remain hidden. Even if there are more like me, I can't risk my own life or anyone else's.

MESSAGE OF DARKNESS

In the year 2029, humanity began to look towards the stars for answers. Earth sent out colonies to try and find a more hospitable place to live. One company, Tevra Corporations, was bent on exploring the stars in their quest to make humanity perfect. In 2021, Tevra had managed to contain what could have been a devastating outbreak in one of their labs. However, many still wonder if Tevra is as benevolent as they say they are. Now, it is 2067 and few hear from those that left for a better life in space now. Tevra has fallen to blame for the potential mass loss of life as many of the spaceships were funded and built by the company. Earth has been known to be uninhabitable and deserted for all space-faring peoples, yet no one knows why.

The captain of a freelance space-pirate crew was one of the earlier groups of people to be sent to space. Many of them against their will. They quickly bonded and will do just about any job, as long as you pay. However, the captain received a signal from Earth as the crew was working on a salvage job in a restricted area.

Captain's Report: #812

Spiegel Station – Mars Sector

The crew has come into contact with an untranslatable signal from Earth. It's been approximately fifteen Earth Cycles since I heard anything from there. Last I heard, Earth was planning on sending more people out to this sector. No one ever arrived. My crew is anxious about getting too close to Spiegel Station. If we get found out that we were doing a salvage job in an area like this, the Derov Corps soldiers on the station will track our ship and give us a hefty fine. The area is cleared for people to fly through, but even leaving your ship is a fineable offence. But I have connections in that station that I need to use. There's something about this signal that is important.

Every Earth Week, any captain of a ship is required to create a Captain's Report. In case of emergencies on-board, the reports act as a second black-box that allows other people to determine more of what happened leading up to on-board disasters. It also provides a way for the human race to have a more varied history should it be wiped out, and a way for the captain to keep track of how long they've been in space. The captain on this particular ship just finished with their contact at Spiegel Station. This contact is known for taking information from Earth and then using it to make laws that heavily restrict spacers across the entire spread of humanity.

Captain's Report: #813

Interspace

After spending an Earth Week at Spiegel Station, I was able to procure a new location for where I can figure out what this signal is actually saying. While I was talking with one of my contacts, they gave me an opportunity. When I translate the signal and determine the exact source, I am to take the information to my contact. I just hope that they won't use it to do something bad. I might not have the best record in the universe, but I do try not to do evil things. I just follow the money. Now, we are set to warp through interspace to our destination. The forest planet Geron. There we should be able to find the equipment we need to translate this message.

It was about ten Earth Cycles ago when this captain first visited Geron. There, he had been hired for a job in the city of Harana. A job that would haunt this captain for many years to come. He remembers what happened in the moments leading up to what he did as he approaches the planet.

Captain's Report: #293

Harana – Forest Oasis – Geron

A storm rolled in. Nothing would happen to the city. With the thick atmosphere, the trees grow to be as big as mountains on Earth. It's been about five and a half Earth Cycles since I became captain of this ship. The previous captain had named the ship The Gilded Quasar. I liked the name, but I never felt like I would be able to live up to it. I served under him as a crewmate, and when he was killed, I took over as captain. I decided to keep the name, but I never wanted to follow in his footsteps. He would go on about how heroic he was, and how he saved an entire galaxy. I wanted a simpler life. One where I could explore the stars. Except running a full spaceship is expensive. So, I had to find work somewhere. Now, I would consider myself and my crew as something along the lines of freelance pirates. As I look out across the city from my quarters in the ship, I see the beauty of it. I might have to rethink my business strategy. But, tomorrow, I need the cash.

Captain's Report: #814

Jusal Station – Geron Sector

The last time I was at Geron, I never thought that what would happen could. The mission was just to set a fire big enough to evacuate Harana so that my business partner could go in and find where the Jewel of the Forest was. I didn't know that the plasma ignitor was tampered with. The tree erupted into flames, and soon after the fire spread to the city. I looked down at Geron and could still see the scorch marks where the fire had been. The entire planet was being engulfed by the flames. It would be at least another thirty Earth cycles before life can return to the planet. A few people still lived on the planet, but most who do are criminals and pirates. Hopefully I can find what I need.

Another five Earth Cycles passed and the captain of this ship cracked the signal and gave the message to their contact. Soon after, no one was allowed in the Origin Solar System. Earth and all planets nearby were under quarantine. Now, the captain felt obligated to see why the message was sent in the first place.

Captain's Report: #1042

Interspace

According to my Earth Sync, today marks the 20th cycle of me being captain. It's also been about five Earth cycles since I received that message. I was able to figure out what I said after a whole cycle. But, by then it was probably too late. I remember it saying something about an unnatural storm. The message described it as black spears falling from the heavens. Whatever the storm was, it has to be too late now for anyone. Especially since no one in the universe has heard anything from Earth. There has been talks that everyone might have to switch their time measurements with no word coming from Earth. Right now, my crew is headed for Earth. The Derov Corps quarantined Earth and its solar system about a year after I cracked the message. The Derov Corps might as well be hiding a city behind a twig. I managed to get a code to access the quarantine zone, but I hope that what I find is worth it after how much I spent getting it. There has to be something here.

Captain's Report #1043

Space – Earth Sector

Everything looked normal, so far. There was a lot less satellite debris surrounding Earth. We passed by the other planets in the solar system, and all of them have gone dark. No one was here anymore. Even the planetary stations have all shut down. At least a few of them were designed to hold people in cryogenic sleep in case we needed more people in the universe. Now, all of them were probably dead. We got close enough to land on Earth, and could see ruined buildings everywhere. To my surprise, there were still people there. At least there should be, according to my sensors. But, I looked around and found nothing. I turned a corner in the town we landed in and saw a wall of ice. No, this was a castle of ice. It had streaks of purple that tingled when I touched them. I told my crew to break through the wall and we found a statue. The ice emanated from the statue. An inky substance was oozing from the statue as well. Every once in a while, it would shoot up through the top of the ice castle and out to somewhere else on Earth. One of my crew members decided to investigate the ooze and got a little too close. It seeped inside of him and he screamed as he fell to his knees. It looked like he was dying. There was nothing we could do. He got up, and started attacking us. The ground itself was moving around him. We tried to kill him, but had to run back to the ship. I never signed up for this. But, something happened to Earth, and I won't be the one to save it.

The captain found an ancient statue that was the source of Earth's demise. From Tevra taking advantage of it, to the statue creating a storm that would fracture humanity on Earth and leave one race left to live. A dark power lurked inside of the statue, but perhaps one day there will be someone that can heal a darkened Earth.

NOTE TO THE READER:

The next, and final, story is separate from the previous stories. While the previous ones are somewhat connected, and I don't have many plans for them at the moment, the following one is completely unconnected. I also do have a plan for this one. You might know that I am currently working on a full-length novel and I am wanting this story to be the start of a new novel. Inspired by the various Cyberpunk content available, this is the story of struggle. Of trials. And of really cool stuff. I sincerely hope you enjoy what I have created so far.

</EDGE OF THE WIRE>

Data driver encrypted. Unencrypt?

Rain crashed on the windshield of the car. Streetlights glowed with a neon amber. The road was empty. Not a car in sight. Tonight was the night. Just one more job, then I can get out of this God-forsaken city.

Job specs: Break into the V.A.T. and copy the data from the guarded server.

- *Do not raise any alarms, alerting the guards will force a system reset and lock down all data.*

- *Get in, and get out. I don't need you looking around at everything. This isn't a tour.*

- *No guns. No casualties.*

The rain will help me keep quiet. But, the V.A.T. is another beast entirely. I've done jobs at other corpobases before, but the V.A.T. is the biggest and most secure. Owned by the Veratech corp, the Veratech Azure Terrace boasts the most advanced security system in the world. No one in their right mind would accept a gig there. Except me. The data driver held information on the guard cycles and their routes. I should be able to sneak in through the subway system with that area lacking guards. The tunnels lead directly underneath the militaristic complex. There is only one entrance and exit to the V.A.T. right at the front gate, but many of the higher-ups will use the tunnels to enter quicker. If I can get on to one of the corpo's trains, then I might be able to squeeze my way in. Luckily, this data driver has a virus on it that forces the subway to call one of the trains.

Stepping out of the car, my black trench coat flowing around my knees, the subway station was only a couple blocks away. Walking there on foot, I managed to think of how I would complete this heist. It was late enough when most civilians would be off the streets, but the homeless would still be around. I hope that they were able to find some sort of shelter for the night. The rain grew stronger as I entered the subway station. I walked up to the ticket kiosk and inserted the data driver and it printed a ticket for platform 0. I turned the corner past the gate and platform 0 was right there. It wasn't much of a platform, but more of a hole in the wall just big enough to enter. The train arrived and I only had 30 seconds to confirm my identity before it would enact security measures. I knew I wasn't in the system of approved riders, so I opened the net link hub. I jack in my personal link and disable the security system. The lights flicker. The train was now invisible to the net. I've had to have done this at least a hundred times by now, yet every time I jack in I worry that it'll be spiked and someone will be able to track me.

The train slows to a stop. The door opens and I'm underneath the V.A.T.

I scanned the area and there's no guards nearby. Only a security camera just past the entrance. I knew that the instructions said no guns, but with this level of security, it wouldn't hurt to have one to take out the cameras. I drew my silenced pistol from my holster. The door opens with the tap of a button, I aim, and the camera breaks.

I open up the included map from the data driver. It calculates my best path to take and I follow it. I walk past empty offices. An elevator goes up to the top of the control tower, but I don't need to go all the way up. I should just need to get to the server floor. Instead of going straight to the server floor, I go to the floor below it. It's just another office floor and there shouldn't be anyone working at this hour. The door opens. Another quick scan. Nothing. So much for the most advanced security system in the world. It can't be this easy, right? I've already reached the stairwell to the server room. I scan inside and see a couple of guards. I check my map again to make sure I know where I'm going.

The location changed? I could have sworn it was on the server floor, but now it's saying that it's above me by quite a bit. It has to be on the top floor. I turn around to go back down the stairwell to reach the elevator when I see something move out of the corner of my eye. I draw my gun and point it at what moved. They looked like they could have been a guard, but their attire didn't match the others. They had the armor of the guards, but they had a long red scarf that almost looked like a cape.

"Whoa, whoa, whoa, let's not be too hasty now," they said calmly with their hands raised up. "I think we can be of use to each other."

"Give me one good reason not to paint this room right now," I said as I pointed the gun right between their eyes.

"You're here for the data on the upcoming product launch, correct?"

"And what about you?" I asked, cautiously. He shouldn't be able to know why I was here.

"Well, I'm here for the prototype. It's just a new cybernetic implant, in a sense."

"Look, I just want to get the data and get out of here. Let's forget that we ever met each other and go on our separate ways." I started to lower my gun to point at the ground.

"Hmm, but I've come all this way just to meet you. Leon."

"Wait a minute, you're. You're Crimson Steel! I should have recognized the cape."

"I'm flattered. So, how did a low time thief get their hands on a gig at the V.A.T.?"

"That's none of your business." I realized that he also shouldn't have known my name. Unless, my reputation has already grown that much.

"Right, right. Just curious. You really shouldn't be here."

"Why's that?"

"Haven't you noticed how easy it's been so far? That would be my doing. Along the path you took to get here, there were ten guards. Not anymore," Crimson Steel said with a smirk on his face.

"You killed them?" I asked, worriedly.

"No! I freed them from their lives of corporate slavery."

"So, you killed them."

"If you wish to see it that way, so be it. Just go get your data and get out of here. If you're still in the complex in five minutes, be prepared." In a flash and puff of smoke, Crimson Steel was gone.

Five minute timer started.

There were no stairs that led to the top floor, so I ran back to the elevator.

4:00 Remaining

The elevator moved quickly and I found myself on the top floor of the control tower. There was someone sitting at a computer, facing away from me. I didn't have time to deal with this. I just needed to find a way to sneak over and grab the data off of that computer. Then I could leave before Crimson Steel comes back.

3:00 Remaining

I scanned the person sitting at the computer.

Ferror Nuitir – Chief of Armed Affairs – Veratech Corporation

This guy is in charge of everything with Veratech's personal military. Of all nights he had to be here, it had to be tonight. I didn't want to kill him, but I needed to get him out of the way. I continued with my scanning and started to remotely hack him. It was a pretty simple hack, just a little something to cause his cybernetics to reboot, which would cause him to pass out for a while. Long enough for me to access the computer.

2:00 Remaining

I jacked in my personal link and started to download all of the files from the computer. I quickly skimmed through the files, and what I was looking for was there. I uploaded the data to an empty data driver I had. This was all I needed to grab, but I saw that the computer was connected to a safe in the room. I unlocked it, and found a bunch of creds, some sort of cybernetic, and an encrypted data driver. All I had to do now was to quickly leave without setting off the alarms.

1:00 Remaining

I got back on the elevator and made my way back down to the lower level where I entered. It felt slower than before. Exiting, I ran towards the train platform past a security control room. Crimson Steel was on the cameras, slaughtering anyone he saw. I looked for the subway train that I took to get here, but it was gone. There was no way for me to leave the complex before the timer-

0:00 Remaining

The ground shook as I heard an explosion come from above. The entire tower had to have collapsed. Were there even any guards left? The train line shut down and the security alarm started blaring. The only way I could try and get out would be if I called one of my own vehicles to my location. It just depends on if they would arrive before Crimson Steel finds me. I called my fastest vehicle. An all-black motorcycle with light blue highlights that can top out at around 300 miles per hour. It would take at least a few minutes for it to get to me, even if it was able to travel at top speed through the city.

Before I knew it, I could hear heavy footsteps coming down to the subway platform. It had to be Crimson Steel. I had hidden myself behind a concrete construction barrier, and I could see him walking towards me. It was plausible that he already knew my location. He was dragging a body alongside him. It was Ferror Nuitir. Crimson Steel entered the subway platform and tossed the body in the middle of the platform.

"I know you're still here. And, I know that you have something that belongs to me," he said in a much more commanding way than earlier.

I didn't respond. My motorcycle was close. Only about another minute or two before it arrived. If I could get on it, I would be home free.

Crimson Steel walked around the platform. His boots echoing with each step he took. There were a few other concrete barriers on the platform. He picked up a barrier and threw it onto the tracks. I could tell that he was frustrated, but it seemed like something else was going on. Were his cybernetics causing him to short-circuit?

"Come on out Leon. If you don't this corpo-slave dies," shouted Crimson Steel as he primed his gun at the head of Ferror Nuitir.

I couldn't just let him kill the chief of armed affairs to one of the most powerful corps in the world. If he dies, we'll both be hunted down till the end of our days. I had no choice. I knew that I wouldn't be able to take him head-on, so I tried to hack him. The soft he's running is too advanced for me to hack into. I had no other options. All I had left was my silenced pistol.

I stood up and pointed my gun at Crimson Steel. His back was turned to me, but he stood there. Motionless.

"You think you can fight me and win?" Crimson Steel said as he turned towards me and started to approach.

"I have to try," I said.

I couldn't see a weapon in his hands, but I couldn't just let him get closer to me when I knew that he was going to kill me.

I shot at his right arm to try and slow him down. I still didn't want to kill him. He kept approaching like nothing happened. Three more shots. Nothing, again. I could see that his armor now had holes in it. Below the carbon-black guard armor was a scuffed silver color.

Realizing that his armor was compromised, he ripped off the right sleeve. Underneath was a silver metal arm. Who knows what kinds of hidden tricks he had in that thing. It looked like what an organic arm looks like without skin, but it was all metal. It was almost like some sort of metal mold that crept all the way up his arm.

He lifted his metal arm towards me and what appeared to be a small cannon popped out from the top of the arm. Before I knew it, an explosion cracked behind and around me, tossing me over the concrete bunker I was hiding behind before. My ears were ringing with a kind of static and my vision became pixelated.

I half expected Crimson Steel to be standing over me, ready to kill me. But, he was just standing right where he was before. Almost like he was frozen.

I got back up onto my feet and started a system diagnosis. Nothing came up in the scan that was urgent, just some minor damage to my ocular and auditorial implants. At least, that's the damage to my implants. I'm not sure of the damage to my organic body, but nothing felt broken.

I walked over to Crimson Steel. He has a pulse, but he isn't responding to anything. His metal arm was still pointed straight out, aiming the rocket cannon. Was there someone else here? He had to have been hacked. He must have left the runner jacked into the V.A.T.'s system.

Unknown hack incoming: 0%

Someone else is here. If I don't eliminate them, or get out of their range quickly, I'll end up just like Crimson Steel. I scanned the area. Nothing.

Unknown hack incoming: 50%

My motorcycle arrived and I hopped onto it. Time to get out of here. In a split-second I was at the exit to the tunnel. The hack was still incoming, but it was slowing down.

Unknown hack incoming: 75%

Not fast enough. I have to get out of their range before I can deliver the data to the person that hired me. Just as I zipped past the city center, the hack failed. It wasn't much farther to get to the meetup point.

This is the place, the Virtical. A place where all sorts of mercenaries and guns-for-hire meet to get gigs from Brokers. It's also a place where your reputation determines what kinds of Brokers you can work for and the gigs they'll give you. The better you are at the job, the higher up you go. Just about everyone here only wants the fame and money that comes with the job.

I was to meet my Broker, Palero, on the 20th floor. The nature of this gig wouldn't boost my reputation much, but it should put me a little bit closer to the 50th floor at the top. Maybe my interaction with Crimson Steel will help push me even closer.

The door opened and Palero was standing, looking out the tinted window. I placed the data driver on his desk.

"Have a seat, Leon," said Palero. "I believe this is yours now." Palero wirelessly transferred the creds to me. He turned to look at me. His shades sat on the tip of his nose as he stared into my very being.

"Is something the matter?" I asked.

"Why was Crimson Steel there tonight?" Palero sat down at his desk, putting the data driver in a drawer.

"I'm not sure. How did you know he was there?"

"I'm a Broker, information's my currency. Without it, I'm nothing."

"You tryin' to tell me that Crimson Steel was supposed to be there?"

"He was. And you weren't supposed to know that he was there, let alone what he was there for."

"Wait, wait, wait. What do you mean by that? I still don't know why he was there, he just ended up killing a bunch of people."

"With that, it is evident you have more information than you need. Something that I can't allow." Palero pulled out a revolver and aimed it right between my eyes.

"You double-crossing, piece of" –BANG–

My sight slowly turned red before my cybernetics started shutting down. Alarms blaring, vision glitching.

"I'm gonna – clean -up -- --- yeah – --- -- room 20-- thank ---"

</DEATHCYCLE>

Before, death used to be calm. Now, it's like all the voices in my head are released at once to drag me down to hell. In these moments before the final end, I'm trapped in my own subconscious. Being able to see digital reconstructions of memories before I fade is bittersweet. Seeing the good things I've done right next to all of the people I've killed wasn't something I expected to see after death. I expected to be met with judgement from a higher being, not from myself. Even now, I can't tell if I regret what I've done with my life, or just numb to it. It feels like it's been eternity, as well as a simple moment. I keep looking through memories, trying to remember what life was like. Who knew life would be exciting and boring?

I've lived through all of my memories, again. And again. And again. And again. Until all of them merge and I forget that I was even dead. Just to have to relive my death over and over and over and over and over and over. My memories. The sum of my choices that all led me to one final outcome. I try to close my eyes to slip into a quiet nothing, but I can still see the lights and memories. It's like I can't let go no matter how hard I try. A repetitive cycle that keeps me from having peace. Maybe this is hell. What better punishment for sin is there than being alone with your mind. Killing you over and over again only for you to be stuck watching everything you've ever done. Every happy moment quickly overshadowed by embarrassment, or pain.

Please, just let me leave.

The cycle continues. I've lost count of how many times I've seen everything. Except this cycle, something is different. I can't tell exactly what it is, but my memories feel almost incomplete, like I gained a new batch that got lost in transmission. Or locked behind the door of a vault. At the same time, I can feel the presence of another. Not of a higher being, but of someone like me.

Dead, yet living.